PIANO

C000151410

The Big Book of Swing!

Hal Leonard Europe

Distributed by Music Sales

Exclusive Distributors:
Music Sales Limited
8/9 Frith Street, London W1D 3JB, England.
Music Sales Pty Limited
120 Rothschild Avenue, Rosebery, NSW 2018, Australia.

Order No. HLE90001001
ISBN 0-7119-8272-4
This book © Copyright 2000 by Hal Leonard Europe.

Cover design by Michael Bell Design.
Printed in the USA.

Your Guarantee of Quality:
As publishers, we strive to produce every book to the highest commercial standards.
The book has been carefully designed to minimise awkward page turns and
to make playing from it a real pleasure.
Throughout, the printing and binding have been planned to
ensure a sturdy, attractive publication which should give years of enjoyment.
If your copy fails to meet our high standards, please inform us and we will gladly replace it.

Music Sales' complete catalogue describes thousands of titles and
is available in full colour sections by subject, direct from Music Sales Limited.
Please state your areas of interest and send a cheque/postal order for £1.50 for postage to:
Music Sales Limited, Newmarket Road, Bury St. Edmunds, Suffolk IP33 3YB, England.

www.musicsales.com

Across The Alley From The Alamo · 4
Ain't Misbehavin' · 10
Alright, Okay, You Win · 12
American Patrol · 7
Angel Eyes · 16
Baby, It's Cold Outside · 22
Beat Me Daddy, Eight To The Bar · 26
Blue Champagne · 19
Boogie Woogie Bugle Boy · 30
Bye Bye Blackbird · 34
Call Me Irresponsible · 42
Ciribiribin · 46
Cocktails For Two · 37
Day By Day · 48
Don't Get Around Much Anymore · 50
Drop Me Off In Harlem · 54
East Of The Sun
(And West Of The Moon) · 60
Everybody Loves My Baby
(But My Baby Don't Love Nobody But Me) · 62
Everything Happens To Me · 66
Fever · 57
Five Guys Named Moe · 70
Flying Home · 77
Hello, My Lover, Goodbye · 82
Hit The Road To Dreamland · 86
Honeysuckle Rose · 94
I Hear Music · 89
I Won't Dance · 96
I'm Beginning To See The Light · 102
If I Had You · 108
If I Were A Bell · 105
If You Can't Sing It
(You'll Have To Swing It) · 112
In The Cool, Cool, Cool Of The Evening · 117
Is You Is, Or Is You Ain't
(Ma' Baby) · 120
It Could Happen To You · 126
It Don't Mean A Thing
(If It Ain't Got That Swing) · 130

The Joint Is Jumpin' · 134
Lazy River · 123
Lean Baby · 138
Leap Frog · 144
Let's Dance · 146
Let's Get Away From It All · 148
Love Is Just Around The Corner · 150
The Man With The Horn · 141
Mississippi Mud · 154
Mood Indigo · 156
Moonglow · 160
On A Slow Boat To China · 164
Opus One · 167
Perdido · 170
Satin Doll · 173
Smoke Rings · 176
Solitude · 181
Struttin' With Some Barbecue · 184
Sugar Blues · 187
Sweet Sue - Just You · 190
'Tain't What You Do
(It's The Way That Cha Do It) · 193
Take The 'A' Train · 196
Taking A Chance On Love · 202
Tangerine · 206
That Old Black Magic · 210
There! I've Said It Again · 199
Tuxedo Junction · 216
When I Take My Sugar To Tea · 220
When Sunny Gets Blue · 224
When The Red,
Red Robin Comes Bob,
Bob Bobbin' Along · 228
When The Sun Comes Out · 234
Witchcraft · 231
Woodchopper's Ball · 238
You Brought A New Kind Of
Love To Me · 241
You're The Cream In My Coffee · 246
Zoot Suit Riot · 248

ACROSS THE ALLEY FROM THE ALAMO

Words and Music by
JOE GREENE

THE AMERICAN PATROL

Music by F.W. MEACHAM

AIN'T MISBEHAVIN'

Words by ANDY RAZAF
Music by THOMAS "FATS" WALLER and HARRY BROOKS

Lyrics:
1. No one to talk with, all by my-self, no one to walk with,_ but I'm
2.,3. (See additional lyrics)

hap-py on a shelf. Ain't mis-be-hav-in', sav-in' my love for

you.

you.

Additional Lyrics

2. Now I know for certain you're the one I love.
   I'm through with flirtin', just you I'm dreamin' of.
   Ain't misbehavin', savin' my love for you. *(To Bridge)*

3. I don't stay out late; I don't care to go.
   I'm home about eight, just me and my radio.
   Ain't misbehavin', savin' my love for you.

ALRIGHT, OKAY, YOU WIN

Words and Music by SID WYCHE
and MAYME WATTS

Moderately, with rhythm

Well, Al - right,_____ O - kay,_____ You Win,_

_____ I'm in love with you.. Well, Al - right,_____ O - kay,_____ You Win,

_____ Ba - by, what can I do?_ I'll_____ do an - y - thing_ you say,_

ANGEL EYES

Words by EARL BRENT
Music by MATT DENNIS

BLUE CHAMPAGNE

Words and Music by GRADY WATTS,
FRANK RYERSON and JIMMY EATON

Slowly

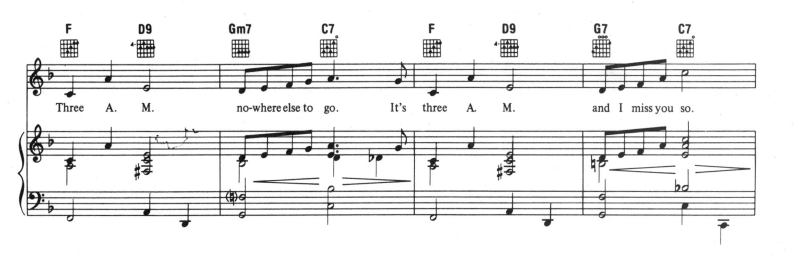

Three A. M. no-where else to go. It's three A. M. and I miss you so.

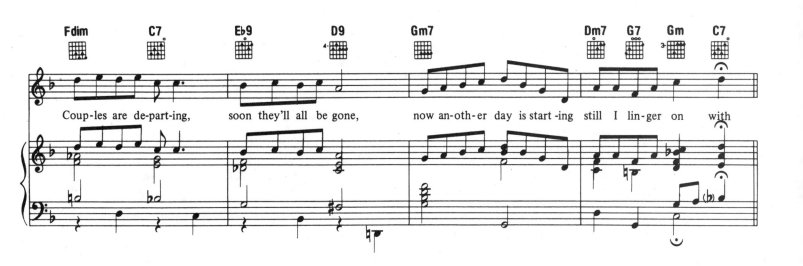

Coup-les are de-part-ing, soon they'll all be gone, now an-oth-er day is start-ing still I lin-ger on with

BABY, IT'S COLD OUTSIDE
from the Motion Picture NEPTUNE'S DAUGHTER

By FRANK LOESSER

23

BEAT ME DADDY, EIGHT TO THE BAR

Words and Music by DON RAYE,
HUGHIE PRINCE and ELEANOR SHEEHY

BOOGIE WOOGIE BUGLE BOY

from BUCK PRIVATES

Words and Music by DON RAYE
and HUGHIE PRINCE

Medium Boogie Woogie

He was a fa-mous trum-pet man from out Chi-ca-go way, ___ He had a "boo-gie" style that no one else could play. ___ He was the top man of his craft

MCA Music Publishing

BYE BYE BLACKBIRD

from PETE KELLY'S BLUES

Lyric by MORT DIXON
Music by RAY HENDERSON

COCKTAILS FOR TWO

from the Paramount Picture MURDER AT THE VANITIES

Words and Music by ARTHUR JOHNSTON
and SAM COSLOW

Oh, what de-light to be giv-en the right _ to be care-free and gay _ once a-gain. No long-er slink-ing, re-spect-a-bly drink-ing like civ-il-ized la-dies and

CALL ME IRRESPONSIBLE

from the Paramount Picture PAPA'S DELICATE CONDITION

Words by SAMMY CAHN
Music by JAMES VAN HEUSEN

CIRIBIRIBIN

Based on the original melody by A. PESTALOZZA
English Version by HARRY JAMES and JACK LAWRENCE

DAY BY DAY
Theme from the Paramount Television Series DAY BY DAY

Words and Music by SAMMY CAHN,
AXEL STORDAHL and PAUL WESTON

DON'T GET AROUND MUCH ANYMORE

Words and Music by BOB RUSSELL
and DUKE ELLINGTON

DROP ME OFF IN HARLEM

Words by NICK KENNY
Music by DUKE ELLINGTON

Drop me off ___ in Har - lem, ___ an - y place _ in Har - lem. ___ There's some - one wait - ing there who makes it seem like

55

FEVER

Words and Music by JOHN DAVENPORT
and EDDIE COOLEY

you all know. Fe - ver is - n't such a new thing,

E7   Am   5 Am

fe - ver start - ed long ____ a go.   burn.

Verse 3   Romeo loved Juliet,
           Juliet she felt the same,
           When he put his arms around her, he said,
           "Julie, baby you're my flame."

Chorus   Thou givest fever, when we kisseth
           Fever with thy flaming youth,
           Fever - I'm afire
           Fever, yea I burn forsooth.

Verse 4   Captain Smith and Pocahantas
           Had a very mad affair,
           When her Daddy tried to kill him, she said,
           "Daddy-o don't you dare."

Chorus   Give me fever, with his kisses,
           Fever when he holds me tight.
           Fever - I'm his Missus
           Oh Daddy won't you treat him right.

Verse 5   Now you've listened to my story
           Here's the point that I have made:
           Chicks were born to give you fever
           Be it fahrenheit or centigrade.

Chorus   They give you fever when you kiss them,
           Fever if you live and learn.
           Fever - till you sizzle
           What a lovely way to burn.

EAST OF THE SUN
(And West of the Moon)

Words and Music by
BROOKS BOWMAN

EVERYBODY LOVES MY BABY
(But My Baby Don't Love Nobody But Me)

Words and Music by JACK PALMER
and SPENCER WILLIAMS

With a beat

VERSE

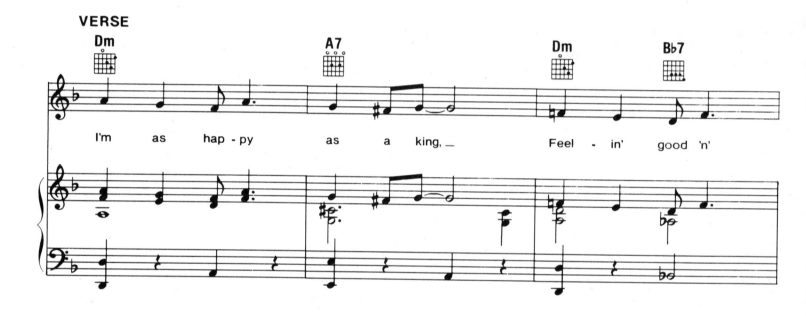

I'm as hap-py as a king, __ Feel-in' good 'n'

ev-'ry-thing. __ I'm just like a bird in Spring, ___

MCA Music Publishing

EVERYTHING HAPPENS TO ME

Words by TOM ADAIR
Music by MATT DENNIS

FIVE GUYS NAMED MOE

Words and Music by LARRY WYNN
and JERRY BRESLER

MCA Music Publishing

FLYING HOME

Music by BENNY GOODMAN and LIONEL HAMPTON
Lyric by SID ROBIN

HELLO, MY LOVER, GOODBYE

Words by EDWARD HEYMAN
Music by JOHNNY GREEN

Love is a leg-end grown dim-mer and dim-mer. There's noth-ing left ___ but the

ti-ni-est glim-mer of hope. ___

Where is the one ___ who will make my life sun-lit? Where is the kiss ___ that will

HIT THE ROAD TO DREAMLAND
from the Paramount Picture STAR SPANGLED RHYTHM

Words by JOHNNY MERCER
Music by HAROLD ARLEN

I HEAR MUSIC

from the Paramount Picture DANCING ON A DIME

Words by FRANK LOESSER
Music by BURTON LANE

HONEYSUCKLE ROSE
from AIN'T MISBEHAVIN'

Words by ANDY RAZAF
Music by THOMAS "FATS" WALLER

I WON'T DANCE
from ROBERTA

Lyrics by OSCAR HAMMERSTEIN II and OTTO HARBACH
Screen Version by DOROTHY FIELDS and JIMMY McHUGH
Music by JEROME KERN

Think of what you're los-ing By con-stant-ly re-fus-ing to dance with me.

___ You'd be the i-dol of France with me! ___ And yet you stand there and

shake your fool-ish head dra-ma-tic-'lly. While I wait here

I'M BEGINNING TO SEE THE LIGHT

Words and Music by DON GEORGE, JOHNNY HODGES,
DUKE ELLINGTON and HARRY JAMES

8vb

IF I WERE A BELL
from GUYS AND DOLLS

Medium Bounce

By FRANK LOESSER

Ask me how do I feel___ Ask me now that we're co-sy and cling-ing___
how do I feel___ From this Chem-is-try les-son I'm learn-ing___

Well sir, all I can say___ is if I___ were a bell___ I'd be
Well sir, all I can say___ is if I___ were a bridge___ I'd be

ring-ing.___ From the mo-ment we kissed to-nite___
burn-ing.___ Yes, I knew my mor-ale would crack___

IF I HAD YOU

Words and Music by
TED SHAPIRO, JIMMY CAMPBELL and REG CONNELLY

IF YOU CAN'T SING IT (YOU'LL HAVE TO SWING IT)

from the Paramount Picture RHYTHM ON THE RANGE

Words and Music by
SAM COSLOW

In the Cool, Cool, Cool of the Evening

from the Paramount Picture HERE COMES THE GROOM

Words by JOHNNY MERCER
Music by HOAGY CARMICHAEL

IS YOU IS, OR IS YOU AIN'T

(Ma' Baby)

Words and Music by BILLY AUSTIN
and LOUIS JORDAN

LAZY RIVER

from THE BEST YEARS OF OUR LIVES

Words and Music by HOAGY CARMICHAEL
and SIDNEY ARODIN

I like la - zy weath - er, I like la - zy days;

can't be blamed for hav - ing la - zy ways. Some old la - zy riv - er

sleeps be - side my door, whis - p'ring to the sun - lit shore.

IT COULD HAPPEN TO YOU

from the Paramount Picture AND THE ANGELS SING

Words by JOHNNY BURKE
Music by JAMES VAN HEUSEN

IT DON'T MEAN A THING
(If It Ain't Got That Swing)
from SOPHISTICATED LADIES

Words and Music by DUKE ELLINGTON
and IRVING MILLS

What good is mel-o-dy, __ what good is mu-sic, __ if it ain't pos-ses-sin' some-thing

THE JOINT IS JUMPIN'
from AIN'T MISBEHAVIN'

Words by ANDY RAZAF and J.C. JOHNSON
Music by THOMAS "FATS" WALLER

Tempo di-sturb de neighbors

They have a new ex-pres-sion a-long old Har-lem way____ that

tells you when a par-ty is ten times more____ than gay.____ To

say that things are jump-in' leaves not a sin-gle doubt____ that

LEAN BABY

Lyric by ROY ALFRED
Music by BILLY MAY

THE MAN WITH THE HORN

Lyric by EDDIE DeLANGE
Music by JACK JENNEY, BONNIE LAKE
and EDDIE DeLANGE

LEAP FROG

Music by JOE GARLAND

MCA Music Publishing

LET'S DANCE

Words by FANNY BALDRIDGE
Music by GREGORY STONE and JOSEPH BONINE

LET'S GET AWAY FROM IT ALL

Words and Music by TOM ADAIR
and MATT DENNIS

LOVE IS JUST AROUND THE CORNER

from The Paramount Picture HERE IS MY HEART

Words and Music by LEO ROBIN
and LEWIS E. GENSLER

MISSISSIPPI MUD

Words and Music by JAMES CAVANAUGH
and HARRY BARRIS

Moderately slow, with a beat

When the sun goes down, the tide goes out The peo-ple gath-er 'round and they all be-gin to shout "Hey! Hey! Un-cle Dud___ it's a treat to beat your feet on the Mis-sis-sip-pi Mud It's a treat to beat your feet on the

MOOD INDIGO

Words and Music by DUKE ELLINGTON,
IRVING MILLS and ALBANY BIGARD

MOONGLOW

Words and Music by WILL HUDSON,
EDDIE DE LANGE and IRVING MILLS

Like some-one that has-n't an-y coun-try, _____ like a strang-er vis-it-ing from Mars, I went a-round a-lone, just like a roll-ing stone un-til I read a mes-sage in the stars:

ON A SLOW BOAT TO CHINA

By FRANK LOESSER

Slowly, with a beat

OPUS ONE

Words and Music by
SY OLIVER

Moderate Jump Tempo

I'm wrack-in' my brain, to think of a name, __ To give to this tune, so Per-ry can croon, __ And may-be Ol' Bing will give it a fling, __ And that 'll start ev-'ry-one hum-min' the thing. __ The mel-o-dy's dumb, re-

PERDIDO

Words by HARRY LENK and ERVIN DRAKE
Music by JUAN TIZOL

SATIN DOLL
from SOPHISTICATED LADIES

Words by JOHNNY MERCER and BILLY STRAYHORN
Music by DUKE ELLINGTON

SMOKE RINGS

Words by NED WASHINGTON
Music by H. EUGENE GIFFORD

SOLITUDE

Words and Music by DUKE ELLINGTON,
EDDIE DE LANGE and IRVING MILLS

STRUTTIN' WITH SOME BARBECUE

Words and Music by LILLIAN HARDIN ARMSTRONG
and DON RAYE

SUGAR BLUES

Words by LUCY FLETCHER
Music by CLARENCE WILLIAMS

SWEET SUE-JUST YOU
from RHYTHM PARADE

Words by WILL J. HARRIS
Music by VICTOR YOUNG

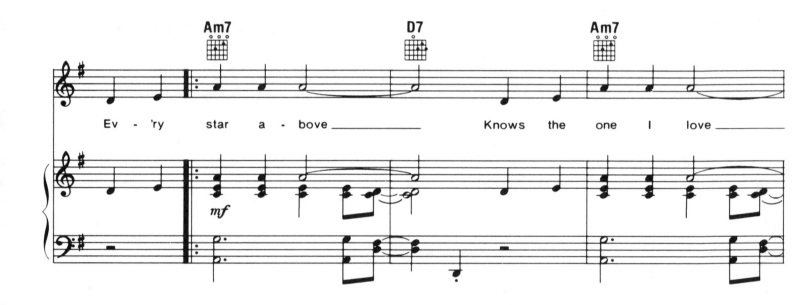

Ev - 'ry star a - bove _____ Knows the one I love _____

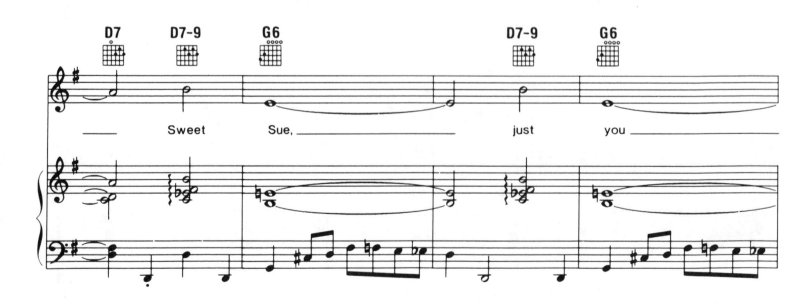

_____ Sweet Sue, _____ just you _____

'TAIN'T WHAT YOU DO
(It's the Way That Cha Do It)

Words and Music by SY OLIVER
and JAMES YOUNG

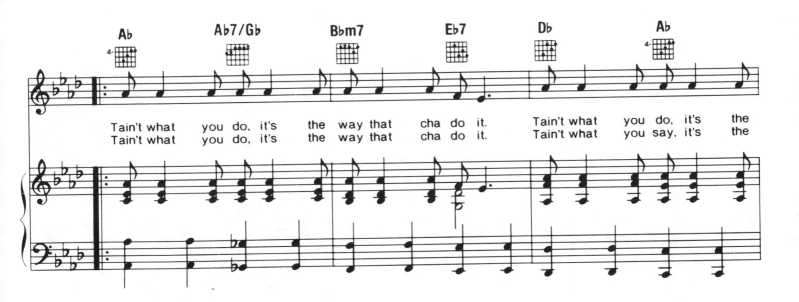

Tain't what you do, it's the way that cha do it. Tain't what you do, it's the
Tain't what you do, it's the way that cha do it. Tain't what you say, it's the

way that cha do it. Tain't what you do, it's the way that cha do it,
way that cha say it. Tain't what you say, it's the way that cha say it,

TAKE THE "A" TRAIN

Words and Music by
BILLY STRAYHORN

THERE! I'VE SAID IT AGAIN

By DAVE MANN
and REDD EVANS

TAKING A CHANCE ON LOVE

Words by JOHN LA TOUCHE and TED FETTER
Music by VERNON DUKE

TANGERINE

from the Paramount Picture THE FLEET'S IN

Words by JOHNNY MERCER
Music by VICTOR SCHERTZINGER

South A-mer-i-can sto-ries ____ tell of a girl who's quite a dream, ___ the beau-ty of her race. Though you doubt all the sto-ries ____ and think the tales are just a bit ex-

THAT OLD BLACK MAGIC

from the Paramount Picture STAR SPANGLED RHYTHM

Words by JOHNNY MERCER
Music by HAROLD ARLEN

TUXEDO JUNCTION

Words by BUDDY FEYNE
Music by ERSKINE HAWKINS,
WILLIAM JOHNSON and JULIAN DASH

WHEN I TAKE MY SUGAR TO TEA

from the Paramount Picture MONKEY BUSINESS

Words and Music by SAMMY FAIN,
IRVING KAHAL and PIERRE NORMAN

WHEN SUNNY GETS BLUE

Lyric by JACK SEGAL
Music by MARVIN FISHER

WHEN THE RED, RED ROBIN COMES BOB, BOB BOBBIN' ALONG

Words and Music by
HARRY WOODS

WITCHCRAFT

Lyric by CAROLYN LEIGH
Music by CY COLEMAN

WHEN THE SUN COMES OUT

Lyric by TED KOEHLER
Music by HAROLD ARLEN

WOODCHOPPER'S BALL

By JOE BISHOP and WOODY HERMAN

MCA music publishing

YOU BROUGHT A NEW KIND OF LOVE TO ME

from the Paramount Picture THE BIG POND

Words and Music by SAMMY FAIN,
IRVING KAHAL and PIERRE NORMAN

Sweet one, _____ fair - er than the flow - ers, _____

YOU'RE THE CREAM IN MY COFFEE

from HOLD EVERYTHING

Words and Music by B.G. DeSYLVA,
LEW BROWN and RAY HENDERSON

247

ZOOT SUIT RIOT

Words and Music by
STEVE PERRY

Original key: Ab minor. This edition has been transposed up one half-step to be more playable.